VERB CHOICES
AND VERB FORMS

DYAD
LEARNING PROGRAM

TUTOR'S BOOK

VERB CHOICES AND VERB FORMS

DYAD
LEARNING PROGRAM

TUTOR'S BOOK

Alice C. Pack

Brigham Young University
Hawaii Campus

NEWBURY HOUSE PUBLISHERS / ROWLEY / MASSACHUSETTS

NEWBURY HOUSE PUBLISHERS, Inc.

Language Science
Language Teaching
Language Learning

Rowley, Massachusetts 01969

Cover design by Christy Pizzo.

Printed in the U.S.A.
ISBN: 0-88377-080-6

First printing: October 1977

5   4   3   2

NOTES FOR THE TEACHER

The Student Dyad Program, using student interaction, clozure, and individual pacing, has many advantages for labs and large classes. It provides the opportunity for a student to participate actively, to receive immediate feedback of correct or incorrect responses after he has responded, and to proceed at a student-selected pace. It also requires social interaction and it provides a built-in incentive for completion of the program.

In the program, the dyads provide both a cooperative and a competitive environment. "Cooperative" because students work together to assist each other in advancing through the steps of the various categories; "competitive" because students strive to complete steps before a completion deadline (the end of the semester during the tryout period) and frequently they strive to complete a step or a category before their classmates. The dyads are also mainly transactional and are thus somewhat more akin to real life situations than many English Second Language programs. The student learns prepositions, pronouns, verb forms, etc. through a constant repetition within the sentence structure. Without focusing attention on syntax, this important aspect of the language is reinforced throughout the Dyad Program as the students read and produce the thousands of sentences that constitute this program. Word order is mastered by the constant iteration of simple (and occasionally complex) English sentence patterns.

Also, the student, in a friendly situation, may have some of the individual frustrations of language learning removed by seeing that others have many of the same problems and difficulties that he has—one of the benefits listed by psychologists in group process.

MATERIAL DESCRIPTION

The materials of the program consist of a corpus of language learning material divided into categories—prepositions and related forms, pronouns and related forms and articles and determiners; verb forms and verb choices; coordinators, etc. Each of these categories has from ten to thirty-four steps, with each step having a minimum of six and as many as ten variant forms.

The steps consist of single sections having a series of unconnected sentences with fifteen clozure blanks in each section. Deleted items in the preposition category are preselected prepositions or related forms. For each blank, students select one from any two to six different stated prepositions, with review sections having unlimited choices. Deleted items in the pronoun category are preselected pronoun or related forms from various classes of pronouns, including subject, object, possessive, and reflexive. The review sections have unlimited choices from all classes previously covered. Deleted items in the verb forms category are choices of forms of *be, have, do,* and the modals. Deleted items in the verb choices category are preselected verb pairs, e.g. *do* and *make, lie* and *lay,* etc. The student's choice for clozure in all categories is determined by the context and syntax of the individual sentence.

PROCEDURAL DESCRIPTION

Students work in groups of two (dyads)—one in the role of tutor and one in the role of respondent. The copy with the correct clozure items listed at the side of the sentences is always for the tutor, and the one with the sentences with only their clozure blanks is always for the respondent, and both should be so used. In the student dyads, participants alternate as tutors and respondents. The program provides the answers, so it is not essential that the tutor know more about English than the respondent. When an odd number of students attends a session, the lab assistant or instructor acts as the tutor in one dyad.

In the operation of this program, students are assigned, when possible, to work with other students who are working in the same category and on steps near each other, with the assumption that a student tutor who had completed that step would have a good review, and a student tutor who had not yet reached that step would have a good preview and learning experience. However, it is not necessary that each member of a dyad even be in the same category. Each could work as a tutor on the respondent's program while acting as respondent on his own, thus alternating categories as well as steps. Again, both students would be learning English skills—either previewing new steps or reinforcing steps already mastered. The way through the program is through completion of the steps of each category of the program. The system is set up so any given student may be a tutor for some other student respondent either before or after he has completed the step the student respondent is on.

After the tutor and the respondent in a dyad receive their copies of the category, the respondent, holding the copy without the correct clozure items, reads the first sentence aloud indicating clozure by filling the blank, or blanks, with the correct word, or words, indicated by the sentence itself. The tutor, holding the copy with the correct clozure items listed, reinforces the respondent's clozure selection when the sentence is read by saying, "mmhmm" with rising intonation [m⌐Mm] if the item is correct, and "mm-mm" with falling intonation ['m⌐'mm] if the item is incorrect (a nonthreatening reinforcement). If the clozure item is incorrect, the respondent again reads the sentence with another selected clozure item. Students alternate as respondent and tutor in each dyad after a respondent has read all of the sentences with their clozure items in one section. Each dyad continues with alternate pages of the same step until one student makes an error-free set of responses on one of the variant forms. (The criterion for determining an error-free set of responses is the completion of a section of fifteen items without any errors on a single complete reading.) Then the student completing the step advances up one step in the program. Upon the completion of one category—that is, finishing each step in that category with an error-free page on a single complete reading—a student proceeds with another category. Students work through each category of the program step by step, from the first to the concluding step. A student may pass as many steps as he is capable of passing in any one session, or he may remain on one step for several sessions. He stays on a step until he completes a fifteen item section without an error for that step.

There may be additional choices for some of the clozures but the preference in the author's dialect is given.

VERB CHOICES

Verb choice clozure is confined to the choice between verbs which students often confuse when confronted with the selection of the correct lexical item. Many students have problems deciding whether to use *do* or *make*. They also confuse the verbs *take* and *bring*. Nearly all English second language students, and many native speakers, have trouble with *rise* and *raise, sit* and *set,* and *lie* and *lay. Bite* and *sting* have been included because Japanese students, especially, have problems as both of these are often equated with their word for *puncture.*

STEPS

1. *Do* and *make*
2. *Go* and *come*
3. *Lie* and *lay*
4. *Sit* and *set*
5. *Rise* and *raise*
6. *Bite* and *sting*
7. *Know* and *understand*
8. *Come, go* and *leave*
9. *Take* and *bring*
10. *Get, make* and *do*
11. *Say* and *tell*
12. *Want* and *need*
13. *Want* and *like*
14. *Want, need* and *like*
15. *Look, watch* and *see*
16. *Listen* and *hear*

1 A   do, make

She ––– the dress herself. At first I –––n't believe she could ––– it.

made; did; do

If he'd ––– his homework when it was first assigned, he'd probably ––– better grades.

do make

He always ––– things well, and so ––– his parents.

does; do

She ––– good grades in school, and ––– a lot to help others too.

made; did (makes; does)

He ——— unhappy until he made some friends.

She ——— a great many opportunities in her life.

He insisted that he ——— heard by the judge.

I would prefer that he ——— all the time he wants.

When we ——— young, we ——— happy.

22 G

I ——— not sure whether he will ——— there or not, as he hasn't ——— there lately.

If I ———n't sure I ——— right, I wouldn't make such a big fuss.

Their home ——— quite small, but they ——— building a new one.

Where ——— all the people last night?

He ——— with that company for a long time and will probably remain with them until he retires.

There ——— a special meeting next Monday to decide who will ——— the next chairman.

When ——— he here last?

They ——— a hard time this past year.

One of the boys ——— sure to win, and one of the girls ——— already won one race.

If you ——— your work promptly, I'll ——— a cake for dinner.   do; make

He ——— many things well, and so ——— his parents.   does; do

The children ——— a lot of noise during the meeting.   made

He was happy he ——— the team.   made

He ——— the best he could.   did

1 B

He ——— well in the tryouts and ——— the first team.   did; made

What ——— you so unhappy here?   makes (made)

She ——— a cake for the boy's birthday.   made

He ——— a bird nest of folded papers.   made

He always ——— that to get attention.   does

It ——— no difference to me which class he takes.   makes

He usually ——— what is right.   does

He ——— some little animals out of the scrap lumber.   made

He ——— a good choice.   made

Usually the teachers ——— their best to help the students.   do

If we ——— what's right, we won't have to ———
apologies for our actions.   do; make

He frequently ——— many things that ——— his mother happy.   does; make
(did; made)

1 C

I ——— my bed every morning while I was there.   made

She ——— her homework before it's due.   does

22 E

I would ——— glad to help if I ——— able to.

There ——— many changes around here since you left.

If I ——— the king I ——— give everyone a holiday.

The eggs ——— boiled for three minutes.

He is unable to come, but he ——— send a substitute.

When ——— you take your last vacation?

When ——— this store open in the morning?

Mother says I ——— go if I finish my work.

One of them ——— here since 1971.

It seems like we ——— here for years.

This paper ——— spots on it.

She ——— trying to reach you for hours.

They ——— a party when we arrived last night.

22 F

When he ——— a little boy, he was quite handsome.

I would ——— glad to help if I ——— able to.

When I ——— able to, I always went to the assembly.

They ——— living there for several years.

Sometimes he ——— some strange ideas.

Since you ——— there, why didn't you stop them?

If there ——— more people like him, the world would ———
a better place.

He ——— more money than I ——— now.   makes; do

He ——— a paper bird by folding a sheet of paper.   makes (made)

She ——— very well in school; in fact she ——— all   did; made
A's last semester.

I cook the meals and she ——— the dishes.   does

She said she could ——— the dress for you next week.   make

He said he would ——— a canoe for you if you would   make
find a good log.

He ——— what is expected of him.   does

What ——— he ——— for a living before he came here?   did; do

How much ——— he ——— last year?   did; make

She ——— all her own clothes.   makes

1 D

He ——— many things with his money.   did (does)

She ——— a sweater with the yarn.   made

He always ——— his homework every night and so ——— his   does; do
friends.

They ——— him president of the group.   made

He ——— the work all by himself.   did

He ——— the toy all by himself.   made

She ——— her own clothes.   makes

He ——— some kites for the boys.   made

She ——— that all the time.   does

He said he could ——— the work himself.   do

He ——— several mistakes on the exam.   made

If I were asked to run it, I would insist that the crane ——— a safety device put on it.

They ——— their books now and can start the lesson.

——— he know what is expected of him?

She ———n't had that very long.

John ——— several accidents this past year.

They ——— surprised to hear the news.

One of the teachers ——— absent for three days.

My mother and father ——— there first.

The clerk asked if he ——— help me.

22 D

He could ——— a good student.

If he ——— happy, he'd smile.

He ——— problems before he came.

One of the boxes ——— opened when it came.

We ——— always had a car.

Mary ——— never had time to do it.

Why ——— they do things like that?

It ——— written by her father last year.

He ——— come whenever he ——— get off work.

——— you finished your work yet?

I'm not sure I ——— go without permission.

She ——— able to do the work until she got sick.

See if the mail ——— delivered yet; it should ——— delivered before now.

Their father ——— sure the boys understood him.   made

If you ——— your work well you will be paid well.   do

He has ——— all the work required for the course.   done

1 E

He ——— beautiful carved figures.   makes

She ——— beautiful dances on the program.   does (did)

She asked me to ——— her a dress.   make

Two and two ——— four.   make

They usually ——— their work well.   do

He often ——— that.   does

He needs to ——— the work again.   do

What ——— him do that?   made

We have finished our work; what should we ——— now?   do

He said he would ——— a copy for us.   make

He ——— a map for the tourists.   made

How many mistakes did you ———?   make

Every day she always ——— the dishes and then ——— her bed.   does; makes

He only ——— what he is told.   does

1 F

He ——— friends easily.   makes (made)

I knew she would ——— a lovely dress because she
——— everything well.   make;
                                                                   does

7

22 B

Half of these apples ——— worms in them.

If I had been happy I ——— have stayed.

It ——— a blemish so they should sell it at half price.

The pictures will ——— taken tomorrow morning.

Half of the rice ——— weevils in it.

He ——— possibly decide to go if we buy him a ticket.

The theme ——— changed by the committee at the last meeting.

What ——— the instructions say about fixing it?

He ——— a man now and should ——— capable of making that decision.

She ——— many problems in her home.

I ———n't seen him lately; I don't think he ——— around for a while.

He ——— have tried harder.

The bananas ——— stolen by someone in the neighborhood.

22 C

He ——— have been here an hour earlier to go with the first group.

If you want the job you ——— have to be on time.

What ——— the rule book say about that?

I have often wondered what I ——— have done in that situation.

We ——— lots of time to finish our work before noon.

They always ――― their homework.	do
He ――― his work well.	did
She ――― many friends while she was there.	made
When I see her ――― so many things well it ――― me feel small.	do; makes
How many friends have you ――― here?	made
They have ――― several small models.	made
She ――― the models out of clay.	makes (made)
Why do you ――― that all the time?	do
She always ――― well in school.	does
Why do you ――― so many mistakes?	make

1 G

Her remark ――― me very happy.	made
His comments were ――― without too much thought.	made
He ――― me feel bad when he said that.	made
She ――― almost everything very well.	does
He's ――― that several times.	done
He's ――― several of those boats before.	made
I wish you'd ――― up your mind.	make
Would you please ――― this for me?	do
He ――― that all the time.	does
He ――― his homework yesterday.	did
If you think you can ――― it, why don't you try?	do
He ――― those all the time.	makes

If I ――― allowed to speak I'd demand that he ―― freed.

If he ――― here he'd change things.

22 A   review of all forms given

Why ――― he always complain about things?

·If he ――― powerful enough he would change the law.

Where ――― you while he ――― examined?

He knew he ――― have to do the work or he would be replaced.

What ――― the last conference accomplish?

I wish he ――― go to the conference.

I wish I ――― go with you, but it's impossible.

Some of them always ――― lots of problems.

The rocks ――― shaded all day long.

All the food had ――― eaten before we arrived.

He said he ――― go if he ――― possibly arrange it.

――― he always dependable?

He ――― have been there because he knows everything that happened.

Let's ——— something different for our projects.	do (make)
I want to ——— something of my life.	make
I want to ——— something during my lifetime.	do

1 H

He has ——— many mistakes in the past and will probably ——— some more.	made; make
One should ——— a plan and then see if he can make his plan work.	make
What ——— him do that?	made (makes)
The boys ——— a large kite.	made
He ——— me mad when he does that.	makes
He is ——— his best.	doing
Have you ——— your work yet?	done
If he has ——— all he can then we will ——— the rest.	done; do
When he wasn't able to ——— it, he quit.	do (make)
How much of the work has been ——— on the project?	done
He ——— very well in the game.	did
He is working on his project, but he isn't ——— very well.	doing
The boys certainly ——— a mess of the house.	make (made)

1 I

She ——— her work every day.	does
What have you ——— to help your neighbor and what are you planning to ——— in the future?	done; do

If he ——— convicted he'd lose his job.

I demand that he ——— a fair trial.

If I ——— in your place, I'd do it.

He requested that he ——— transferred.

He wondered if he ——— dreaming.

She insisted that the machinery ——— a safety device.

I asked that he ——— given some help.

I felt so homesick that I wished I ——— back home.

He moved that the vote ——— postponed.

He desired that I ——— released and I know if he ——— here,
I'd be free.

If everyone ——— present we'd vote.

21 F

If he ——— lucky enough to win, he could quit work.

I demand that smoking in this room ——— stopped.

He requested that everyone present ——— allowed to vote.

She'd want to go home too if she ——— homesick.

They all wish they ——— back home.

I wish I ——— out of this situation.

He insisted that his wife ——— allowed to talk to him.

She asked that she ——— given something to eat.

I wondered if he ——— being considered for the job.

I insist that he ——— the same privileges that I have.

I'd tell him what to do if I ——— consulted.

His only wish was that she ——— there too.

You will have to ——— up your mind quickly.   make

If he ——— an error he will have to do his work again.   makes

Mother ——— a pie for dinner.   made

Did you ——— your work?   do

He ———better last year in school than he is ——— this year.   did; doing

She ———her little girl a dress yesterday and plans to ——— her   made; make
another one tomorrow.

He told me that he was ——— his best to finish his project.   doing

She ——— me promise that I wouldn't do that again.   made

Who is there among us who ——— everything right?   does

What did you ——— with my things?   do

1 J

He ——— his work well.   does

He ——— all the furniture in this room.   made

She ——— costume jewelry.   makes

They ——— their homework last night.   did

We ——— a lot of things today.   did (made)

She usually ——— that job.   does

Mary ——— all her own clothes.   makes (made)

Bill always ——— the dishes.   does

He ——— a living selling insurance.   makes (made)

She ——— a lot of mistakes on the exam.   made

Please ——— certain you haven't forgotten anything.   make

Bill always ——— his best.   does

He insisted that he ——— released.

The man demanded that he ——— some representation.

21 D

What would you do if he ——— given your position?

I wish I ——— ten years younger.

He requested that he ——— advanced in rank.

What would you do if it ——— your son?

He wished that he ——— given the same chance.

Her husband insisted that she ——— some time off.

She wishes she ——— in Europe too.

She requested that she ——— transferred.

He isn't here today, but he wishes he ———.

He demanded that he ——— given the right to go.

I'm not a doctor, but if I ——— I'd put you in the hospital.

If he ——— in charge he'd insist that things ——— run differently.

I insist that they all ——— released immediately.

He asked that he ——— given time to consider the proposal.

21 E

Her mother isn't here, but if she ——— she'd fix things up.

If I ——— in charge, things would be different—I'd insist that the people ——— heard.

Mary always ——— the best she can.   does

How many items does that ———?   make

Please ——— me a favor.   do

1 K

I have ——— up my mind to do it.   made

He ——— a model of the ship.   made

He ——— well in his schoolwork.   does (did)

She ——— a lot of good for mankind.   does (did)

I think they should ——— away with all the red tape.   do

Your suggestion ——— sense.   makes (made)

Mary ——— the cooking.   does (did)

He'll ——— some excuse for being late.   make

The president ——— the speech.   made (makes)

I wish she'd ——— up her mind about it.   make

She ———things I couldn't do.   does (did)

Please ——— certain he's there.   make

We ——— many things while we were there.   did (made)

Have you ——— your homework yet?   done

He ——— without a lot of things.   did (does)

What would you do if he ––– in charge?

He requested that he ––– given a vacation.

He suggested that they ––– released immediately.

If I ––– you, I'd take his advice.

Supposing she ––– in my shoes; what would she do?

Perhaps if he ––– here, he'd do it.

His mother implored that her son ––– released.

Most of the people preferred that the man ––– a hearing.

21 C

I insist that I ––– allowed to call my lawyer.

If he ––– powerful enough he would change the law.

I would be glad to help if I ––– able.

I ask that I ––– given more time to finish.

If there ––– time enough we'd hear from everyone.

He recommended it ––– discussed at the next meeting.

If I ––– young again I wouldn't be as carefree.

If there ––– more people like him the world would be a better place.

He moved that the meeting ––– adjourned.

If the house ––– on a hill it would have a lovely view.

If he ––– right we'd all be wrong.

I ask that he ––– given some consideration because of his age.

I request that I ––– permitted to speak.

2 A go, come

She ——— here frequently.	comes (came)
They ——— to town yesterday.	went
We are ——— to town tomorrow.	going
He is ——— to see us tomorrow before he ———.	coming; goes
He said he was ——— to do it, but he hasn't done it yet.	going
He was here a short while ago, but he's ——— now.	gone
Be sure and ——— to the show here tomorrow night.	come
I don't know where they have ———.	gone
He ——— and goes at will.	comes
Although he was late, he ——— over anyway.	came
How many people plan to ——— to our party?	come
Everyone is ——— to our school to see the play.	coming
He asked me when I was ——— to the show with him.	going
She has ——— with him several times already.	gone

2 B

Everyone in the family ——— to school now.	goes
They usually ——— to all their meetings.	go
She has ——— to see them every Sunday since she came.	gone
How soon do you think you can ——— over?	come
How many times have you ——— there?	gone
How often do you ——— swimming?	go

21 A subjunctive forms

I wish I ——— able to go, but it's impossible.

If I ——— a millionaire, I'd buy a yacht and sail around the world.

If I ——— asked to comment I would insist that everyone ——— the same opportunity to speak.

If your father ——— here you wouldn't act like that.

The people insisted that the judge ——— impeached.

I sometimes wish I ——— able to live the past year over again.

She requested that she ——— given a hearing.

He demanded that the case ——— reviewed.

If I ——— the judge, I think I'd find him guilty.

If she ——— going, I'd go too.

He demanded he ——— given the right to speak.

The woman demanded that she ——— equal opportunities.

If he ——— happy, he'd smile.

21 B

I know I could do it if I ——— allowed to.

I'd do it if I ——— you.

He insisted that he ——— released.

The judge insisted that the man ——— an attorney.

If he ——— here I'd go.

He demanded that he ——— heard.

If I ———n't sure that I was right I wouldn't make such a fuss.

He has ——— there several times during the past month.   gone

She never ——— unless someone takes her.   goes

How can we ——— if the car won't run?   go

They ——— immediately when she called.   went

They are ——— out in a few minutes.   going

I was ——— there, but I've changed my mind.   going

Several people ——— to the party last night.   went (came)

The medical team ——— to many countries of the world on their last trip.   went

The mayor ——— out of his way to help the people of his city.   goes

2 C

I'll ——— and take my sister with me.   go

He ——— to see us several times.   came

He ——— away last year, but he's ——— back.   went; coming

He never seems to seek honors; they just ——— to him.   come

He always ——— to see me on Fridays.   comes

She often ——— to see her other friends too.   goes

He ——— to school every day during the semester.   goes (went)

First set a goal and then ——— after it.   go

He never ——— to class yesterday and didn't ——— today either.   went; go (came; come)

Let's ——— to the show tonight.   go

Who is ——— to bring the food?   going

All things finally ——— to an end.   come

He ——— to Japan for his vacation.   went

He would come if he could, ——— he?

Mary couldn't come, ——— she?

They brought the food, ——— they?

We'd better hurry, ——— we?

20 F

They haven't been here very long, ——— they?

She doesn't sew very well, ——— she?

He's here every day, ——— he?

They weren't at the party, ——— they?

He brought the food, ——— he?

He paints very well, ——— he?

Mary always does her homework, ——— she?

We won't have to go, ——— we?

We shouldn't have to do that, ——— we?

You can't do that, ——— you?

Her parents were here, ——— they?

He has to go, ——— he?

He hasn't had that very long, ——— he?

Bring your girl friend with you, ——— you?

He wouldn't make it, ——— he?

2 D

He ——— to this place every year.	comes
Where did he ——— yesterday?	go
He likes to go fishing when the tide ——— in.	comes
She ——— to see us frequently.	comes
Be sure and take all my things with you when you ———.	go
She likes to hunt for shells when the tide ——— out.	goes
Here in the library, one must ——— in the front door and ——— out the back.	come; go
They ——— after the show started, stayed a few minutes, and ——— out before it was over.	came; went
He ——— to high school before he came here.	went
She ——— over to see her friend before she ——— over to see me last night.	went; came
She'll be very unhappy when he ——— back to school.	goes

2 E

I ——— to see her yesterday for the first time.	went
She ——— there frequently, but I have never been.	goes
She often ——— over here to see me.	comes
I'd better ——— and do what he wants.	go
He's not sure when he's ——— abroad.	going
They usually ——— here for their vacation, but occasionally they ——— to the beach.	come; go
Let me know when he ——— in so I can see him.	comes

They shouldn't furnish all the food, ——— they?

It doesn't flood here in the rainy season, ——— it?

John and Mary brought their friends, ——— they?

The washer isn't broken, ——— it?

They should be here, ——— they?

He had to go to town, ——— he?

They've been here before, ——— they?

He's broken his leg, ——— he?

Mary makes her own clothes, ——— she?

John hasn't a care in the world, ——— he?

20 E

They won't come, ——— they?

He's thought of it, ——— he?

You'll bring it, ——— you?

He's coming, ——— he?

She's swimming in the meet, ——— she?

They want to succeed, ——— they?

Mary quit, ——— she?

John went to the party, ——— he?

He should go, ——— he?

They shouldn't be playing there, ——— they?

John can swim, ——— he?

She ——— out for lunch at noon.	goes (went)
Most of the students ——— to school for ten months of the year.	go
He wishes he were ——— here to school instead of ——— abroad.	coming; going
Let me know when the mailman ——— as I have a letter to post.	comes
If he ——— before noon, bring him directly to my office; after that I'll be ———.	comes; gone

2 F

When the sun ——— down, the full moon ——— up.	goes; comes
I'll ——— and bring my brother with me.	come
The train is late; it should have ——— long before now.	come
He often ——— to my house to see my mother.	comes
I ——— once last year, but I'm certainly not ——— again.	went; going
I don't know why the students can't ——— to class on time as they don't have any trouble getting ready when they're ——— on a date.	come; going
Bring all my things with you when you ———.	come
He brought most of my things when he ——— and took all of his with him when he ——— back.	came; went
I don't think I will be ——— with you tomorrow.	going
He ——— in for a few minutes but ——— right out again.	came; went

23

20 C

They tried their best, ——— they?

He's not sure he can come, ——— he?

Many of them were late, ——— they?

He usually succeeds, ——— he?

We're supposed to go, ——— we?

You'll be there, ——— you?

We have always gone, ——— we?

He never succeeds, ——— he?

She's sick, ——— she?

He hasn't any, ——— he?

They bought it, ——— they?

He'll go, ——— he?

We have some, ——— we?

The typewriters are broken, ——— they?

She has several of them, ——— she?

20 D

John's father came, ——— he?

His mother isn't coming, ——— she?

They have a new car, ——— they?

They brought their children with them, ——— they?

He can't do that work, ——— he?

3 A   **lie, lay**

She is ——— on the bed.	lying
She ——— there all day yesterday.	lay
Just ——— the books on the table.	lay
The books are ——— on the table.	lying
He is ——— the silverware on the table now.	laying
She said she would ——— the materials on the table.	lay
I think I'll ——— here all day.	lie
I wish he would ——— his things somewhere else.	lay
I feel like I've ——— on this bed for weeks.	lain
She ——— the things on the table yesterday.	laid
I ——— there for quite awhile before I felt like getting up.	lay
She was ——— on the bed when I saw her last.	lying
The things were ——— on the table when I saw them last.	lying
She was ——— the papers on the table when I came in.	laying
The chickens ——— five eggs yesterday.	laid

3 B

The chicken was ——— on its back.	lying
Just ——— the eggs on the table.	lay
I'm going to ——— down for a while.	lie
Please don't ——— that dirty thing on my clean table.	lay
My brother was ——— bricks for the garage.	laying

You have lots of assignments, ——— you?

They haven't come, ——— they?

It should be done, ——— it?

They don't have any, ——— they?

It's late, ——— it?

He won't be there, ——— he?

He'll be there, ——— he?

20 B

They have finished, ——— they?

Some of them are here, ——— they?

She isn't here, ——— she?

He quit, ——— he?

He has some of them, ——— he?

It's all done, ——— it?

Most of them have come, ——— they?

Mary isn't coming, ——— she?

You have some, ——— you?

Bring yours, ——— you?

He hasn't come yet, ——— he?

It's complicated, ——— it?

Try harder, ——— you?

He passed, ——— he?

There were twenty students there, ——— there?

Your book is ——— on the hall table.   lying

I have been ——— here on the couch all day.   lying

He ——— the paper on the porch.   laid

The old cemetery ——— just north of the church.   lies (lay)

If he ——— there much longer he'll go to sleep.   lies

He always ——— his things on that shelf.   lays

Those things have ——— there for days.   lain

He ——— there without moving for about twenty minutes.   lay

He has always ——— the reports on the table.   laid

I have seen her ——— on the beach for hours.   lie

3 C

He has ——— there for the past three hours.   lain

I feel like I could ——— here forever.   lie

Where did you ——— my book?   lay

John is ——— on the sofa in the living room.   lying

The books are ——— all over the room.   lying

He ——— on the bed and rested before he left.   lay

Just ——— the package on that small table.   lay

He said he would ——— it by the door.   lay

You look tired. Why don't you ——— down for awhile?   lie

The hen has ——— an egg nearly every morning.   laid

It has ——— there for a long time.   lain

He usually ——— down every afternoon.   lies

If they ––– hurry we'll be late.

Neither Mary nor her mother ––– be here.

There ––– a bit of the food left.

I ––– think about it if I were you.

He ––– do anything but sit there day after day.

––– be late or we'll miss the show.

He ––– do anything to help them now.

I'm sure they ––– intending to go.

Not one of them ––– here yet.

Why ––– she tell her mother about it?

Hopefully, they ––– lose their money.

––– bring that up again!

That ––– have anything to do with the subject we're discussing.

20 A   question tags

He's coming tomorrow, ––– he?

They finished their work, ––– they?

You won't be here next week, ––– you?

They're planning a party, ––– they?

He shouldn't do that, ––– he?

You're finished, ––– you?

He likes it, ––– he?

Most of the people were ——— on their beds when the explosion occurred.   lying

He ——— there without moving for a long time.   lay

He ——— his books on the table and went out.   laid

3 D

He was ——— in a hammock enjoying the breeze.   lying

He looked like he had ——— there for hours.   lain

He ——— there for quite awhile without moving.   lay

Just ——— your things anywhere you'd like.   lay

He ——— all his things on the table when he came in.   laid

Why don't you ——— down for awhile and rest?   lie

The storm tipped the table over and it was ——— on its side.   lying

I haven't had a chance to ——— down all day.   lie

She is ——— in bed and intends to stay there all day.   lying

That old board has ——— there for the past week.   lain

He ——— his things down and went outside.   laid

Bring your things over here and ——— them on the table.   lay

The old dog just ——— in the sun and never moves.   lies

She is ——— all your things on your bed.   laying

I can't ——— on my right side any more.   lie

He ——— able to be here last time.

We ——— neither the time nor the money to participate.

No one ——— come yet.

19 E

I'm not sure, but I ——— think so.

Why ——— he go yesterday?

John ——— think he'll go tomorrow.

Mary ——— go today and ——— think she'll go tomorrow either.

One of the boys ——— have his book yet.

Why ——— he come last night?

I ——— have a thing to wear to the party tonight.

She ——— think much of it.

——— he have that finished yet?

Why ——— he hurry up?

Mary ——— even try to answer the questions on the test.

——— he get that finished?

When ——— he hungry?

Why ——— he come tomorrow?

19 F

Why ——— they brought the things yet?

Why ——— somebody do something about it?

3 E

See if you can't get her to ——— down for a while.	lie
She ——— down for a while and went to sleep.	lay
——— your books on that shelf.	Lay
She hasn't ——— down since the storm started.	lain
He doesn't want to ——— his things down because he might forget them.	lay
He ——— his things down and then went off without them.	laid
He was just ——— his things down when I came in.	laying
She said she was just ——— down for a while.	lying
He's been ——— there for hours.	lying
She ——— around the house all day long without doing anything.	lies (lay)
You hung that picture so that it's ——— on its side.	lying
He ——— the groceries on the table and then went out.	laid
That book is still ——— just where you left it.	lying
She ——— in a coma for several days after the accident.	lay
Bring your things over here where you can ——— them down.	lay

3 F

Most of the swimmers were ——— on the sand although a few were ——— on their backs floating in the water.	lying; lying
I don't see how you can ——— around all day and do nothing.	lie
I don't know where you want all these things ———; shall I just ——— them here on the bed?	laid; lay

Some people ——— enjoy active sports.

You'd better hurry as there ——— much time left.

We ——— going with the group tomorrow.

The team ——— had much practice.

I ——— think I'll go.

Mary ——— remember what she is to bring for the dinner.

We ——— have any assignments today.

I ——— getting anywhere with my work until you helped me.

There ——— a single one left.

You ——— ready for the test yet.

19 D

They never ——— come to see us.

She ——— been here for a long time.

He ——— say when he was coming.

——— you see him yesterday?

I ——— do it all by myself.

He ——— coming tomorrow.

Why ——— you plan on going tomorrow?

He ——— never been late to class.

There ——— been any meetings held this month.

I ——— do that if I were you.

There ——— many people at the last meeting.

——— he ever been late to class?

Why don't you ——— down for a while and rest?	lie
I think I'm all tired out because I've ——— here so long.	lain
Who ——— all these things on the table?	laid
He ——— there for a long time without moving.	lay
She was worried because her daughter just ——— there without moving.	lay
He said he would ——— all his cards on the table.	lay
After eating such a big meal, everyone just wanted to ——— around and rest.	lie
She ——— around all day without doing anything; I wish you could get her to do something.	lies
The hen ——— an egg nearly every day.	lays
He ——— on a board at night because he says it helps his back.	lies

4 A   sit, set

Ask the students to ——— down.	sit
Most of the women usually ——— quietly and wait.	sit
In the etiquette class we learned how to ——— the table.	set
The president ——— at his desk every afternoon.	sits
The baby is ——— in his high chair.	sitting
My grandfather always ——— at the head of the table.	sits
Every day mother ——— the china in its proper place.	sets
John is able to ——— the spokes of the wheel just right.	set
Each night the astronomer ——— the telescope on Venus.	sets

19 B

He ——— here right now.

The boy ——— work yesterday.

He ——— working now.

He ——— worked for a long time.

There ——— anything left when I got there.

Most of the students ——— do their homework.

——— he save any money while he was there?

One of the boys ——— here yet.

She ——— lived here since January.

I ——— think you're right, but I'll check.

We ——— have to go unless we want to.

There ——— much use for us to go now.

Neither Bill nor John ——— his work regularly.

There ——— many students at the assembly.

There ——— seem to be any reason why we shouldn't go.

19 C

He ——— being considered for the job.

We ——— heard from him for a long time.

Most of the men ——— hear the order when it was given.

One of the girls ——— come very often.

Neither you nor he ——— nominated.

Everyone ——— around crosslegged on the floor at the party.	sat
Does the director want us to ——— the stage like that?	set
The old hunter often ——— the meat in the freezer.	sets
Government economists sometimes ——— prices.	set
He was ——— in his usual place at the head of the table.	sitting
The farmers don't usually ——— the chickens on the eggs.	set

4 B

When do the birds ——— in the tree?	sit
She was ——— on the porch waiting for me.	sitting
The works of a clock can be ——— by an old watchmaker.	set
A sculptor's model always ——— very still.	sits
The family must ——— still for the photograph.	sit
The judge is old but sometimes he still ——— on the bench.	sits
We have a TV set that just ——— and is never turned on.	sits
I thought he ——— the prices rather high.	set
The letters on the printing machine are often ——— crookedly.	set
That old clock has ——— in that corner for years.	sat
She ——— the hen on the eggs.	set
He ——— there for hours without moving.	sat
Call the babysitter and tell her to ——— with the kids.	sit
Barbara is so popular that she never ——— alone at lunch.	sits
——— the food in the trays and clean the kitchen.	Set

Some of the students ——— get their work in on time.

Why ——— she stay home by herself when she could be here with us?

——— it have to be done today?

19 A

negatives—forms—
don't, doesn't, didn't, hasn't,
haven't, hadn't, isn't, aren't, wasn't,
weren't, won't, wouldn't can't,
couldn't, shouldn't,
with present or past forms
when negative is given by
never, neither, **etc.**

He ——— been there for a year and ——— want to go there again.

My friend never ——— returned things on time.

I wonder why she ——— answer my letters.

I ——— neither the time nor the money to take part in that sport.

Why ——— he here yet?

I ——— go swimming because I ——— bring my bathing suit.

He ——— bring the materials we need.

We ——— had much rain lately.

He ——— seem to care what happens to him.

One of them ——— finished yet.

They ——— bought their texts because the book store ——— have them in yet.

4 C

Tell the children to ——— in their places.	sit
He ——— the furniture on the porch and it's ——— there ever since he left.	set; sat
Haven't you ——— the plates out yet?	set
That old man ——— in the park every day.	sits
That girl ——— at home every night.	sits
——— the pencils in the drawer.	Set
That old couch has ——— there for years.	sat
They often ——— there hour after hour.	sit
The mechanic was able to ——— the gears of the car in place.	set
The guard ——— in the guard shed every night.	sits
Who ——— the prices on this food?	sets (set)
Why don't you ——— the chair on the floor?	set
Every day the bird watcher ——— the binoculars on his favorite tree.	sets (set)
No one ——— there any more.	sits

4 D

Why don't you ——— over there in the easy chair?	sit
Grandpa ——— in that chair every day while he was visiting.	sat
The baby can't ——— alone yet.	sit
He was ——— on that limb of the tree when he fell.	sitting
——— your things down for a while and rest.	Set

Why ——— he take so much time?

Although he can't go he ——— want to be invited.

——— everybody want to go?

——— we have to finish this before we can go?

Why ——— you come home so late last night?

Where ——— this river run to?

Where ——— all the food you bought go?

Mary won't call, nor ——— she want anyone to call her.

Why ——— you do it all by yourself?

I don't care what she says, I know I ——— call her.

I ——— want to be remembered by all of you.

18 F

——— your father have all the help he needs?

I ——— want to call her today sometime.

Why ——— she always call me at work?

That boy really ——— think a lot of you.

Where ——— all the time go to?

Where ——— you spend your vacation last year?

Why ——— they do that?

I ——— listen to my parents occasionally.

Mary ——— think a lot of him at one time.

What time ——— the sun rise in the morning?

——— your friend go with you on the hike?

——— any of the students ever get there on time?

He ——— that machinery up every day.	sets
He was ——— up the materials when he fell.	setting
She ——— down very hard when the chair broke.	sat
She is ——— over there in the corner pouting.	sitting
Everything was all ——— up ready for us.	set
He has ——— there for a long time without speaking.	sat
He usually ——— the firewood up a certain way so it will catch fire easily.	sets
Who ——— behind you in class?	sits (sat)
Grandpa always ——— in this chair.	sits
I wonder who will ——— at the head of the table.	sit

4 E

She ——— the things on the table yesterday.	set
Every night his wife ——— the food on the table.	sets
——— down in that chair over there.	Sit
She is ——— for her portrait.	sitting
He's just ——— there reading the newspaper.	sitting
She ——— there for quite a while before she got up.	sat
The printer's devil ——— the type for the newspaper.	sets (set)
She's ——— in the corner all by herself; I wish someone would go over and ——— by her.	sitting; sit
He just ——— on the chair and never said a word.	sat
She is ——— the table for dinner now.	setting
You must ——— very still or the picture will be blurred.	sit

18 D

I really ——— think it's a good idea. What ——— you think of it?

Perhaps he ——— want it after all.

When ——— the train leave?

When ——— John and Mary expect to go?

Why ——— they always take so long?

Why ——— the project take so long to finish?

Where ——— they go on their vacation?

——— I have to finish this today?

Why ——— I have to finish it so soon?

I ——— think about it, but I still don't want to go.

He ——— listen to his parents, but he still has to make up his own mind about things.

What time ——— the plane usually come?

Why ——— they leave everything with you?

He ——— say he would do it.

18 E

Why ——— he always do it that way?

I ——— want to go although I'm afraid I can't.

——— she do everything she could to prevent the accident?

He really ——— like you very much.

He ――― his things down and went over and ――― in the hammock.   set; sat

I don't think the children can ――― still.   sit

4 F

The food ――― there and no one touched it.   sat

They ――― the stage for the play.   set

The prices are ――― by someone else.   set

He sometimes ――― there for hours without speaking.   sits

She ――― the food on the table, but no one touched it.   set

She ――― there for quite a while without moving.   sat

――― the clock so it shows the correct time.   Set

He was just ――― there when I saw him last.   sitting

I have ――― here so long I'm stiff.   sat

She was ――― the music for the concert on the stands.   setting

All the students came in quietly and ――― down.   sat

The old clock just ――― on the shelf; it has ――― there since grandmother brought it here.   sits; sat

Have you ever ――― for a portrait?   sat

The old cat just ――― there and licks her paws.   sits

I'm sure he ——— think about serious things occasionally.

Where ——— they live?

When ——— the performance start?

——— these things interest you?

——— you attend the meeting yesterday?

——— you think you can do it?

What ——— he tell them about the project?

I've already told you, I ——— too do it.

What ——— the rule book say about that?

What ——— the instructions say about fixing it?

18 C

Why ——— he always complain about things?

When ——— you take your last vacation?

——— this place appeal to you?

Why ——— people act the way they ———?

When ——— the next train leave for the city?

——— they get all their work done on time?

——— he ever get there on time?

Where ——— everyone at the picnic come from?

It really ——— matter to me what you say.

Why ——— the trains always arrive at the same time?

Where ——— the money for the project come from?

I ——— think it matters.

What ——— the last conference accomplish?

I'm telling you again, I ——— complete my work yesterday.

5 A   rise, raise

The sun ——— in the east.	rises
They ——— the new flag over the capitol.	raised
Everyone ——— when the President comes in.	rises
He ——— from his chair when she came in.	rose
They have ——— flowers for years.	raised
He ——— prize flowers for a hobby.	raises
It's customary to ——— your hand before asking a question.	raise
He ——— early every morning.	rises
The sun ——— at 7 A.M. and set at 6 P.M. today.	rose
Why don't you ——— the window and let in some air?	raise
The contractor said they would be ——— the walls on the new building soon.	raising
The flag ——— slowly as the people sang the National Anthem.	rose
He ——— the heavy weights and won the contest.	raised
He ——— and lowers the flag every day.	raises
I like to watch the moon ———.	rise

5 B

My friend always ——— when women come into the room.	rises
It's warm in here. Please ——— the window.	raise
The sun ——— at 7:15 yesterday morning.	rose
He ——— his hand but the teacher didn't call on him.	raised
Yeast makes the bread ———.	rise

18 A
do as auxiliary—
do, does, did

––– you think he should go tomorrow?

––– he go yesterday?

––– his roommate have a book he could loan him?

––– we have to go to the meeting today?

––– you go yesterday? I –––.

When ––– this store open in the morning?

What time ––– the sun go down at night?

Why ––– she stay home last night instead of coming to the party?

I certainly ––– do my work yesterday.

What ––– all of the boys think about this?

People ––– listen to him occasionally.

Why ––– that always have to happen when we're in a hurry?

––– John have all the material he needs?

––– I have to do it today?

18 B

Why ––– she do things like that?

––– you think you could do it?

––– he know what is expected of him?

Why ––– they do things like that?

Mary doesn't sing nor ––– she play the piano.

I ——— early this morning and took a long walk.	rose
He ——— the flag as the group sang the National Anthem.	raised
The water ——— with the tide.	rises
My father ——— many different crops.	raised (raises)
He always ——— early.	rises
When he gives you the signal ——— the banner.	raise
When he came into the room everyone ——— to his feet.	rose
My father has ——— a big wheat crop for several years.	raised
At dinnertime the smoke ——— from all the chimneys.	rises
She was unable to ——— from her chair.	rise

5 C

He is ——— wheat on his acreage this year.	raising
Why didn't you ——— your hand to answer that question?	raise
The sun and the moon both ——— in the east.	rise
Why didn't you ——— when she came into the room?	rise
He ——— lots of corn last year.	raised
The bread ——— to double its bulk in an hour.	rose (rises)
She is ——— her family without any outside help.	raising
They ——— the flag at 8 o'clock.	raised (raise)
The flag ——— quickly when he pulls the ropes.	rises
During the past hour the bread has ——— to twice its bulk.	risen
He has ——— and lowered the flag every day since he came.	raised
He is ——— to great heights in his company.	rising

I ——— too much to do since I came here.

He ——— called before the committee.

I ——— not take any more time off this week.

He might ——— finished first if he ——— run harder.

He ——— that old car for years.

I ——— like to have seen the game, but it was impossible to get away.

One of my parents ——— called every day.

17 F

I wish he ——— come back and given us a report.

They ——— a party next week to celebrate.

Both of them ——— finished the exam already.

Our team ——— the best of all those who competed.

Why ———n't you finished your work?

He ——— trying to upset us.

She ——— aware of the consequences when she did it.

He ——— a successful businessman ever since he graduated.

They ——— coming tomorrow at three o'clock.

No one in the class ——— finished the assignment.

She is the only one who ——— any trouble.

Everyone ——— plenty of time to do the assignment.

He might ——— come if he ——— encouraged to do so.

The least she ——— have done was to call me.

When the boy let out the string the kite ——— high above the   rose
buildings.

They ——— the roofing material to the top floor by means   raised
of a pulley.

He always ——— early in the morning.   rises

5 D

Hot air usually ——— to the top of the room.   rises

The smoke ——— rapidly after he lit the fire.   rose

He ——— his hand before he asked the question.   raised

It's hard to ——— potatoes here.   raise

He ——— early and went for a walk.   rose

The bread has ——— high enough to put in the oven.   risen

When the president came in, everyone ——— to his feet.   rose

If you'd ——— the blinds it would be lighter in here.   raise

He tried hard to ——— the heavy weights.   raise

Let's go for a walk and watch the moon ———.   rise

They ——— and lower the flag by means of a pulley.   raise

When they voted on the question, we all ——— our hands.   raised

They have ——— the price for the show.   raised

I don't think any fish will ——— to that bait.   rise

Every morning he ——— early and goes jogging.   rises

17 D

One of the girls ——— late this morning.

Half of the students ——— unhappy with the present program.

They ——— planned to go yesterday but ——— unable to make it.

He ——— finished before I ———.

There ——— too many accidents around here.

The sun ——— too hot to go outside yesterday.

The man who ——— speaking is my father.

He could ——— tried for his crimes.

He ——— have been punished.

He ——— a hard time trying to convince her that he ——— do the job.

Where ——— you yesterday?

——— Nancy prepared for her talk last week?

17 E

We ——— a late lunch when he called.

Come and see me when you ——— more time.

They ——— a lot of practice this past month, so they should ——— in top condition.

One of the girls ——— some trouble with her back this past week.

He ——— planning on coming tomorrow.

I ——— all mixed up about the plans.

5 E

At eight o'clock the bell rings, the flag ———, and everyone sings the National Anthem.	rises
He was so weak he could scarcely ——— his hand.	raise
That picture needs to be hung higher; why don't you ——— it about six inches?	raise
Gentlemen used to ——— when ladies came into a room.	rise
She enjoys her garden and ——— some lovely flowers.	raises
The building is ——— rapidly.	rising
They expect to ——— their prices.	raise
He has ——— a number of questions about the project.	raised
When the curtain ———, the show is about to begin.	rises
He ——— the flag in his hand and waved it wildly.	raised
He is ——— wheat on his farm.	raising
They ——— the car with a block and pulley.	raised
I don't think anyone ——— that question.	raised
I think I'll ——— early tomorrow and go for a hike.	rise
The balloon was ——— rapidly above the crowd.	rising

5 F

He was always the first one to ——— his hand when a question was asked.	raise
He will ——— to great heights in politics.	rise
She always ——— wonderful tomatoes.	raises
He ——— before the cock crows in the morning.	rises

I ——— have gone if I'd wanted to.

He should ——— told us about it.

When do you think we ——— go?

He ——— some marvelous experiences in his past life.

We ——— always happy then.

He hasn't ——— back since he left.

All of the students ——— on time this morning.

Many years ——— passed since then.

17 C

He ——— there last week when we ———.

We ——— more practice than he ———.

We ——— have gone if we had known about it.

He ——— there more often than I have.

I ——— go if you go.

The food ——— eaten very quickly.

He should ——— gone to the meeting.

I ——— waiting for a long time and I'm tired.

One of the girls ——— late for the practice last night.

Most of the girls ——— on time every day.

He ——— a lot of trouble since he came.

When ——— she here last?

The temperature ——— rapidly after the sun came out.   rose

She ——— the hem on her dress because it was too long.   raised

The ducks ——— quickly from the pond and were soon out of sight.   rose

They ——— the flag every morning over the schoolhouse.   raise

He has ——— vegetables for years.   raised

She has ——— early all her life.   risen

The kite ——— so high we could scarcely see it.   rose

Why did you ——— when he came into the room?   rise

He is ——— a big fuss about the new rule.   raising

Steam is always ——— from the hot pools.   rising

They have ——— the price for the show.   raised

6 A   bite, sting

The mosquitoes ——— me while I was at the picnic.   bit

A bee ——— me yesterday.   stung

Be careful or that dog will ——— you.   bite

That's a wasps' nest, be careful you don't get ———.   stung

This won't hurt, but it may ——— a little.   sting

If a poisonous snake ——— you, it can be fatal.   bites

I wouldn't like that bumblebee to ——— me.   sting

He was ——— by a scorpion.   stung

17 A
review of all forms
previously given

We ――― here for hours.

I ―――n't seem him lately; I don't think he ――― around.

He ――― here several times before I left.

They ――― ready to begin right now.

I'm sure he ――― happier before.

He ――― a lot of problems.

He ――― a man now and should ――― capable of making that decision.

Where ――― you while he ――― examined?

He ――― problems before he came here.

――― you finished your work yet?

He could ――― a good student.

These shoes ――― a good fit.

17 B

I wish I ――― remember her name.

He ――― here for a little while, but I don't know where he ――― now.

She hasn't ――― much fun this past year.

Ask her if she ――― go tomorrow.

He ――― here ever since I can remember.

This will ――― remembered for a long time.

When it opened its mouth, I was afraid the animal
would ——— me.   bite

She screamed when the bee ——— her.   stung

Cleopatra died when a snake ——— her.   bit

He has several large welts where the mosquitoes ——— him.   bit

How many times have you been ——— by a bee?   stung

A mosquito ——— a man and gets nourishment from his   bites;
blood, while a bee ——— him and dies.   stings

6 B

They have a mean dog who ——— anyone who enters the yard.   bites

The medicine ——— when he put it on my sore.   stung

I didn't see the mosquito which ——— me.   bit

A bee can only ——— once.   sting

He has a toothache and can't ——— anything.   bite

He was very ill because a scorpion ——— him.   stung

He says the rash on his arm ———.   stings

It doesn't really hurt, it just ———.   stings

He was ——— by the dog when he went into the yard.   bitten (bit)

That dog is mean; he ———.   bites

Have you ever been ——— by a mosquito or ——— by a wasp?   bitten (bit);
                                                                 stung

Bees only ——— when they are disturbed.   sting

The last time I was in Florida I was ——— by a bee and ———   stung; bitten
by dozens of mosquitoes.   (bit)

Mother says I ――― go if I finish my work.

I ――― like to go, but my work isn't finished.

I'm not sure I ――― go without permission.

I wish I ――― go with you, but it's impossible.

16 F

I ――― go if I had the opportunity.

Bring them over here so we ――― count them all.

It ――― happen although it has never happened before.

If she had liked the country she ――― have stayed.

I ――― go immediately or I ――― be too late and I really ―――n't want to miss it.

If he is elected he ――― do a good job.

He ――― have been here before now; we really ―――n't wait any longer.

It ――― never have happened if you had been here.

If you go I think I ――― probably go with you.

If he were here he ――― know what to do.

――― anyone who wants to enter the contest?

If he had been here he ――― have fixed things up.

6 C

I was afraid the dog would ——— me.	bite
What happened when the bee ——— you?	stung
He hopes the fish will be ——— today.	biting
She yelled when the wasp ——— her.	stung
Use some repellent so the mosquitoes won't ——— you.	bite
He was ——— several times by a ferocious dog.	bitten (bit)
The bees have ——— him before.	stung
My arm ——— where the mosquito ——— me.	stings; bit
He was ——— by a manta ray while he was swimming.	stung
Those fish will ——— at anything.	bite
Does your dog ———?	bite
Where did the bee ——— you?	sting
A bee ——— when he is disturbed.	stings
He's a very friendly dog; I don't think he'll ——— you.	bite

6 D

It ——— when I put the medicine on.	stung
The fish are ——— today.	biting
It itches where the mosquitoes ——— me.	bit
Have you ever been ——— by a dog?	bitten (bit)
Be careful or those bees will ——— you.	sting
It ——— when the doctor gave me a shot.	stung

——— I enter the contest?

I ——— go immediately or I ——— be late again.

If I am elected I ——— do my best to serve.

He ——— have been here an hour ago; I don't think I ———
wait any longer.

It ——— never have happened if I had been there.

When he goes I ——— probably go with him.

Wherever she is I ——— try to find her.

If he were here he ——— do the right thing.

16 E

They ——— never have done it if I had been there.

If I had been the king I ——— have given everyone a holiday.

How many times ——— we forgive others?

If I had been happy I ——— have stayed.

If I were the king I ——— give everyone a holiday.

If I am elected I ——— do my best to serve.

He ——— have been here an hour ago.

We ——— find her at home if she isn't at the office.

Most of the students ——— have done better on the exam.

I ——— be there tomorrow if they need me.

He ——— possibly decide to go if we buy him a ticket.

These large mosquitoes really ———.   bite

He's a vicious dog—he ———.   bites

While he was there a centipede ——— him.   bit

Some people are allergic and have severe swelling when a bee
——— them.   stings

The boy was hungry and quickly ——— into his sandwich.   bit

Have you ever been ——— by a scorpion?   stung

The alcohol ——— when I put it on the wound.   stung

I wish the fish would ——— today.   bite

If a bee ——— anyone, it dies.   stings

6 E

She was ——— by a bee yesterday.   stung

That dog is really mean. He has ——— me twice.   bitten (bit)

This medicine may ——— a little when I put it on.   sting

Did the bee ——— you?   sting

The wasps were ——— everyone at the picnic.   stinging

Don't feed the bears or they might ——— you.   bite

She was ——— several times by yellow jackets.   stung

When these mosquitoes ———, they leave large welts.   bite

I wish the fish were ——— today.   biting

Put some lotion here where the mosquito ——— me.   bit

The bees buzzed angrily around but didn't ——— anyone.   sting

Have you ever been ——— by a centipede or ——— by a   bitten (bit);
scorpion?   stung

16 C

He ––– have been here an hour earlier to have gone with the first group.

I ––– have finished my work last night because I have no time today.

I think I ––– have won if I had entered the race.

I'm sure he ––– do the job if he tries.

He is not sure whether he ––– go or not; he ––– have to ask permission.

––– I have permission to go with them?

She ––– have enjoyed going with them and ––– have if she had known in time.

If you want to keep the job you ––– have to work hard.

She said she ––– come whenever she gets off work.

If I had been there I ––– have helped her.

If I had been the king I ––– have given everyone a holiday.

He ––– be here in an hour; we'll have to hurry with our work or we –––n't go with him.

16 D

I ––– go if I were you.

If I were the king I ––– give everyone a holiday tomorrow.

Ask your mother if you ––– go.

It has never happened before, but if things were just right it ––– happen.

If I had been happy I ––– have stayed.

That dog is always ——— people.   biting

Did many bees ——— you while you took out the honey?   sting

6 F

I don't like bees; they ———.   sting

It really doesn't hurt—it just ——— a little.   stings

If the dog hadn't been chained, it would have ——— me.   bitten (bit)

You'll really be sick if you're ——— by a manta ray.   stung

It was a large centipede which ——— him.   bit

Be careful as there are snakes around which might ———.   bite

Bees ——— when they are disturbed.   sting

If there's a mosquito around, it will ——— me.   bite

He broke his tooth when he ——— into the hard candy.   bit

The fish aren't ——— today.   biting

When a mosquito ———, it sometimes ———.   bites; stings

The manta ray ——— him when he stepped on it.   stung

Be careful of the scorpions; they ———.   sting

They took him to the doctor when the centipede ——— him.   bit

He ――― come whenever he ――― get off work.

See if you ――― arrange your affairs to be there.

If I had been there I ――― have helped her.

16 B

He knew he ――― have to do the work or he would be replaced.

He ――― have come but he didn't want to.

He knew he ――― study or he'd fail the course.

He is unable to come, but he ――― send a substitute.

He didn't know whether he ――― come or not.

I don't think I'd worry about it; however, it ――― be important to someone else.

It ――― have been a disaster, but everything turned out all right.

Everything ――― have been wonderful if you had been there.

I have often wondered what I ――― have done in that situation.

――― I go with you?

He ――― have been there because he knows everything that happened.

He ――― have tried harder.

Things ――― have been different if he had been able to go to school.

He ――― be here tomorrow if he can.

I ――― learn what is expected of me or I'll lose my job.

7 A   **know, understand**

Do you ――― the way to the airport?   know

Although I've read the chapters, I still don't ――― the lesson.   understand

I don't ――― either of them; they're strangers to me.   know

I don't ――― math at all.   understand

He ――― how to drive a car but he isn't a very good driver.   knows

Because he once lived in a ghetto, he ――― the feelings of   understands
those who live there now.

I ――― how to crochet, but I can't ――― the directions.   know;
                                                                      understand

Do you ――― the rules of the game?   know

Do you ――― how to ride a horse?   know

I can ――― the directions, but I still don't ――― how to   understand;
finish it.   know

I thought I ――― what he said even though he was speaking   understood
in another language.

I ――― it by heart, but I forgot it when I saw the huge crowd.   knew

He ――― better than anyone else what is expected of him.   knows

7 B

I thought I ――― the lesson, but I flunked the exam.   knew

I couldn't ――― him because he spoke too softly.   understand

Althouth I've ――― him for years, I really don't ――― him.   known;
                                                                      understand

I don't ――― how to do that math problem.   know
                                                                      (understand)

61

If he ——— spare the money, we ——— certainly use it.

They bought some new furniture although they really ———n't afford it.

We ——— have expected him to do that.

The show ——— be over by now.

It looks like it ——— rain.

Do whatever you think ——— be done.

You ——— have thought of that before you came.

He ——— do anything for her.

16 A   modals, present and past—
can, could, shall, should, may,
might, will, would, must

He ——— have known he would get into trouble.

He ——— have been here an hour earlier to go with the first group.

I ——— have finished my work last night because I have had no time today.

I think I ——— have won if I had entered the race.

I'm sure I ——— do the job; just let me try.

If I had been there earlier I ——— have gone with them.

I'm not sure I ——— go; I ——— have to ask permission.

——— I have permission to go with them?

I ——— have enjoyed going with them.

If you want the job you ——— have to be on time.

He ——— how to drive a car, but he wasn't a
very good driver.   knew

Because he has never lived in a ghetto, he can't
——— the feelings of those who live there.   understand

I couldn't ——— the directions.   understand

Do you ——— how to type?   know

I thought I ——— the directions, but I don't ——— how to   understood;
construct the model.   know

I ——— what he's saying even though he's speaking in another understand
language.   (know)

I ——— his situation, but I really don't ——— how to help him. understand;
                                                             know

He ——— what is said to him, but he doesn't ——— how to   understands;
answer.   know

7 C

I ——— the formula, but I don't ——— how it works.   know; under-
                                                             stand (under-
                                                             stand; know)

Did you ——— the question on the exam?   understand
                                                             (know)

He says he can't ——— the younger generation.   understand

I think I ——— how it works, but I don't ——— for sure.   understand;
                                                             know

Some students have an accent and it's hard to ——— them.   understand

I wish I ——— what he said in his talk; unfortunately, I don't knew;
——— Japanese.   understand

How much do you ——— about their plans?   know

He ——— most of the students well, and he's ——— many of   knows; known
them for years.

15 E

I thought he ——— swim better than that.

If he had told me about it, I ——— have been able to help him.

He ——— speak English well because he's studied it for years.

I ———n't do that again for any amount of money.

Everyone ——— attend the meeting this afternoon.

He ——— have discussed it with me before he sent in the report.

It ——— not sell because of the flaw in it.

I ——— have helped him if I ——— have.

He ——— apply for the job early if he really wants it.

If he ——— do his best, I know he ——— succeed.

When you bring the things over, I ——— like to see them.

He ——— bring his class over to see the program.

Most of the students ——— like to see their grades.

15 F

What ——— you do if that ever came up?

I don't know what ——— have been done that wasn't.

We ——— support her by going to the concert tonight.

Don't get wet or you ——— catch cold.

The plumber ——— repair the pipe before noon.

We ——— have brought a map; now we're lost.

How well did you ——— the lecture?   understand

I ——— the facts but didn't ——— how much they meant.   knew;
                                                           understand

7 D

I wish I ——— what he was talking about.   knew
                                                           (understood)

He mumbles so that I can rarely ——— him.   understand

Could you ——— the teacher this morning?   understand

He ——— the whole thing by heart.   knows

She thought she ——— all the facts, but she didn't.   knew

Do you ——— how that machine works?   understand
                                                           (know)

I don't ——— how to help him although I really   know;
——— his situation.   understand

He thought that no one ——— him.   understood

He ——— the rules, but he didn't obey them.   knew

I'm sure she ——— what's right and what's wrong.   knows

He says he doesn't ——— anyone here.   know
                                                           (understand)

Listen carefully and try to ——— what he says.   understand

I know he ——— me when I spoke to him.   understood

I thought I ——— the speaker, but I'm not sure.   understood

I ———n't think he'd want to go.

He ——— surprise you and do better than you think.

He promised he ———n't do it any more.

How many pencils ——— there be in a box?

You ——— count them if you wanted to.

I said I ——— try and be there on time.

If you ——— make up your mind then we ——— give them our decision.

15 D

I ——— like to have gone, but I didn't have the money.

I don't think it will, but it ——— happen.

He never ——— remember figures, even when he was young.

You ——— have answered her letter before you left.

What ——— have happened if you hadn't helped him?

You ——— do your homework every night.

If I thought I ——— help you, I ———. You know that.

I ——— have known you'd be right.

You ——— have known better.

What ——— a person do when something like that comes up?

I ———n't do anything to help myself as I was helpless.

What ——— you have done in my situation?

They ——— have been here by now.

I wonder who ——— have helped them with the problem.

7 E

It isn't necessary to ——— how it works if you ——— how to run it.	understand; know
I ——— he was listening, but I don't think he ——— what was said.	know; understood
He said he ——— everyone at the party.	knew
He ——— more than anyone thinks he does.	knows (understands)
I thought you ——— how to fix this.	knew
I think I'll drop the class as I don't ——— anything.	understand
Can't you ——— me when I talk?	understand
I ——— he'll do whatever you tell him to.	know
She said she would read the instructions and try to ——— them.	understand
I still can't ——— why she did that.	understand
I don't ——— what he'll do next.	know
Many of them seem confused and don't ——— what to do.	know
He ——— enough not to do that.	knows (knew) (understands) (understood)

7 F

I can't ——— anything about him.	understand
She ——— I want to see her, but she avoids me.	knows
Most of them ——— what they wanted.	knew
I have ——— him for years.	known
She said that no one ——— her.	understood

15 B

Both of us ——— have known better than to do that.

I ——— have gone if I'd wanted to.

Because of my busy schedule I really ———n't take the time to go. However, I'm going.

He ——— have finished that piece long ago if he'd tried.

I ——— consider going if all my expenses were paid.

When ——— we plan on leaving to get there on time?

I ———n't get away any sooner although I had planned to leave earlier.

Although he tried he ———n't make it.

I ——— like to go to the dance tomorrow.

When do you think you ——— do it for me?

He doesn't seem to be able to do it although I thought he ———.

We ——— try and observe all the rules while we're here.

I said I ———, although I wasn't sure.

He ——— have told me about it earlier so I ——— have done something about it.

15 C

They ——— have left earlier, but the car wasn't ready.

Many of the boys ———n't make it today.

I ——— have been there, but I ———n't arrange the time.

If I ——— have helped him I ——— have.

I'm not so sure, the other team ——— beat us.

Can you ——— what she's trying to say?	understand
I ——— what he wants even if I can't ——— him.	know; understand
I thought I ——— the directions, but I don't ——— what to do now.	understood; know
I'm sure he ——— everything we're saying.	understands
I ——— he wants to come, but he won't ——— anything at the convention.	know; understand
Can you ——— these directions?	understand
He should have ——— what was expected of him.	understood (known)

8 A   come, go, leave

My father usually ——— for work at 7:00 a.m., but this morning he didn't ——— until 9 o'clock.	leaves; go (leave)
It's a beautiful spot; we must ——— here when it isn't raining.	come
I need to ——— to the store today.	go
He ——— to work early this morning.	went
He often ——— into our room to show us his new books before he read them.	came
We must ——— here before it starts raining.	leave
Mary has to ——— home early in the morning to get to school on time.	leave
Our neighbors ——— over to visit us once a week.	come
John ——— to the movies almost every week while he was in school.	went

My mother says I ——— go if your mother ——— let you go.

He ——— have been blind not to see that car coming.

I ——— report this to my supervisor.

He's not sure whether anyone ——— get away this afternoon.

15 A   modals, past—
could, should, might, would

He asked if he ——— help us.

I wasn't sure whether I ——— offer to help or not.

I ——— go if I ——— arrange things at home.

There's a possibility that he ——— have been working here last year.

If I thought I ——— have done it, I ——— have tried.

I ——— always study better when I lived at home.

I ——— rather have hired Bill but he wasn't available.

You ——— have asked for a recommendation.

They ———n't give the workers a raise so a strike was called.

He ——— rush to the door when his father came home.

He ———n't find work there last summer.

He ———n't finish the work because he was ill.

I think we ——— leave right away.

Sometimes I ——— to class without my books.   go

The mailman ——— at about 11:00 a.m. every day.   comes

The bus to Honolulu ——— in this direction.   goes

You must ——— there some day when it isn't raining.   . go

His father ——— home from work very late every   came
night last week.

8 B

John ——— for class at 7:15 a.m, so he should be on time.   left

He always ——— with a new girl.   comes

Mary feels sick so she's ——— early.   leaving

This morning she ——— the house early to see the doctor.   left

She was late as she ——— to class at 9:00 o'clock this morning.   went (came)

Our friends never ——— over to visit us.   come

The doctor ——— home from his office and then ——— out   came; went
again immediately.

My sister ——— to the mainland last year for a short visit, but   went;
——— back again to go to school.   came

Mary ——— here two months ago and ——— to New York.   left; went

You've missed your friend; he ——— about five minutes ago.   left

We missed each other; he ——— out one door and I ——— in   went; came
the other.

71

14 E

If I ——— make it, I'll be there by four o'clock.

He says he ——— definitely finish the project.

I ——— or ——— not go; it depends entirely on the weather.

They say they ——— pay well if someone ——— do the job.

Some of the students ——— leave tomorrow, but others ———
complete some assignments before they ——— go.

If he has time he ——— go with you.

I have definitely decided I ——— accept the job.

My sister is planning to go if she ——— get the money.

I ——— arrange to pay for it, but I ———n't find the time
to go.

We ——— seriously consider your proposition.

14 F

I told him he ——— finish the assignment immediately.

I ——— certainly go if I have the opportunity.

They ——— see the ocean from their house.

He says he ——— leave most of his things here until he
comes back.

Bring me some lunch when you come back if you ———.

They say we ——— take two bags with us if we ——— carry
them both.

She ——— have lived here at one time.

They ——— travel extensively this year.

He says he ——— swim well.

8 C

My father ——— for work at 7:00 a.m. although he usually doesn't leave until 9.	left
I have ——— to the store every day for the past week.	gone
He ——— to work at 7:00 every morning last week.	went
The bus ——— Kahuku every 30 minutes.	leaves
Sometimes he ——— into our room to show us a new book.	comes
It started to rain after we ———.	left
Mary ——— home early in the morning to get to school on time.	leaves (left)
Our neighbors used to ——— over and visit us every week.	come
John ——— to the movies almost every week.	goes
Sometimes I ——— my books at home, but I'm usually sorry I ——— without them.	leave; came (left)
You must ——— here some day when it isn't raining.	come
His father ——— home from work very late every night.	comes
Many of the students ——— from a foreign country and were homesick.	came

8 D

John ——— for class at 7:15 a.m. every morning.	leaves
The professor ——— into the room and showed us a new book.	came
Mary felt sick yesterday afternoon, so she ——— home from the office early.	went
Bert ——— to his class at 8 o'clock, but it was a holiday.	went
The new neighbors ——— to visit them regularly.	go (went)

He thinks he ——— go, but he's not sure.

——— I ask your name, please?

If you ——— provide a car, I ——— bring the food for the picnic.

I ——— predict one thing about the race. Our car ——— beat yours.

Many of the students ——— drop the course before the end of the semester.

14 D

I ———n't be there before noon but ——— come as soon as possible.

The work ——— wait until you get back.

I ——— not come here again.

When ——— the visitors arrive?

They ——— be here soon.

He ——— do it by himself if he tries.

I ——— get this done immediately or it will be too late.

He is sure he ——— do it alone.

He ——— bring the things with him.

I ——— do it soon, but I ———n't give you the exact time.

Ask your mother if you ——— go with us.

He says he ——— come as soon as he possibly ———.

Our friends ——— over to visit us.   came

My sister ——— home late from work.   came

John ——— to school on the mainland last year.   went

He ——— Utah in April and ——— over here to live.   left; came

She missed the bus; it ——— five minutes ago. However,   left;
another one should ——— in about thirty minutes.   come

We will have a big crowd to register if everyone ——— at the   comes
same time.

I don't think I can ——— with you this week as I ——— every   come (go); went
day last week.

8 E

He ——— out just a little while ago, but should be ——— back   went; coming
before long.

He ——— for work early this morning.   left

The bus to Honolulu ——— from that direction.   comes

I'm afraid you've missed him; he ——— about an hour ago.   left

The bus is ——— to pick us up.   coming

The bus for town is ——— in half an hour.   leaving (coming)

He has ——— out, but should be back before long.   gone

When he ——— in be sure and tell him I need to see him.   comes

He seems to ——— out every time I ——— in.   go; come

She ——— here and ——— to California.   left; went

Be sure and take your things with you when you ———.   leave

He never ——— over to see us any more.   comes

We missed him when he ——— away.   went

14 B

I'll see if I ——— arrange to do it for you.

I ——— go if I receive an invitation.

The office ——— be closed by then.

We ——— be able to arrange something for you.

He ——— have passed the entrance exam.

Why don't you go and ask her if she ——— go with us?

We ——— be there in about a half an hour.

Some of the students ——— do the assignment without help while others ——— need some assistance.

——— I borrow your car this afternoon?

You ——— borrow it if you ——— drive.

He ——— do the work or he ——— fail the exam.

What time ——— you arrange to be here?

14 C

Let me know if you ——— be there by eight o'clock.

You ——— be very tired after your long trip.

I ——— give you the last chance.

I ——— have made a mistake in my figures.

I ——— understand most of it, but you ——— have to explain a few things.

Let me know if you ——— be able to come.

Many questions ——— be answered at the meeting.

8 F

He doesn't usually ——— before seven o'clock.	leave (come) (go)
She ——— over there quite often.	goes
If we ——— about seven we will get there on time.	leave
He has ——— all this work for me to do.	left
I wish you'd tell him about it when he ——— in.	comes
The bus ——— every hour on the hour.	leaves (comes)
She ——— over here so she could have some peace.	came
I should ——— over there and see him sometime today.	go
Close the door when you ———.	leave
I should have ——— there last week.	gone
Bring me something to eat when you ——— back.	come
Most of the students have ——— home for the holidays.	gone
If you ———, take these with you.	go
Most of the students ——— before I did.	left (came)
They have ——— here several times before.	come

9 A   take, bring

I will ——— the class next semester.	take
He said he had ——— the books to the library.	taken
Please ——— your books with you.	bring (take)

Some of the students ――― trouble with this assignment,
but I ―――n't ――― any.

He ――― a hard time learning English.

He ――― many interesting experiences in his life.

She ――― here since early yesterday.

The queen of the ball ――― selected right now.

14 A   modals, present—
                    can, shall, may, will, must

The wheel ――― turn for the car to go.

Ask him if he thinks he ――― do the work.

I ――― go if I receive an invitation.

Let's go to the show; we ――― do the assignment tomorrow.

There's an emergency, so I ――― leave for home right away.

I ―――'t think when you rush me that way.

I ――― or ――― not go, depending on the circumstances.

Why ――― you always interrupt me?

I will attempt it, but I ――― fail.

How many of you ――― promise to come?

He ――― swim very well because he practices every day.

I ――― give you my answer tomorrow.

If he said he would come, he ―――.

I ――― make a decision tomorrow.

We were told to ——— a lunch with us.   take (bring)

The gift ——— me much pleasure.   brought

He asked if he could ——— his sister over.   bring

He is ——— several courses at school.   taking

Mary is ——— the food for our picnic.   bringing

He ——— my hand and talked to me.   took

Several of the men ——— their wives to the meeting.   brought (took)

Are you ——— your wife with you to that meeting?   taking

What did you ——— me?   bring

Who ——— the papers on the table?   took

Why did you ——— that here with you?   bring

What are you ——— with you when you go?   taking

9 B

What should I ——— on my trip?   take

He ——— his medicine regularly.   takes (took)

I ——— too many things with me on this trip.   brought

I ——— too many things on my last trip.   took

How much money did you ——— for the gift?   bring (take)

The doctor said to ——— two pills three times a day.   take

Be sure and ——— your warm coat tonight.   bring (take)

Where should I ——— these things?   take

Don't hurry; ——— your time.   take

He ——— us some lovely gifts from Europe.   brought

Have you ——— your medicine?   taken

We ——— plenty of time to finish the work.

She ———n't ——— as good as she knows how to be.

It ——— a long time since she ——— here.

They ——— a party when we arrived last night.

He ——— a hard time doing his work.

They ——— trying to reach you for hours.

When we asked about them, we were told that they ———
there earlier but had left.

John ——— several good opportunities for work.

We ——— enough of this foolishness.

It ——— a long time since we've seen him.

There ——— many changes around here since you left.

See if there ——— a mail delivery yet.

13 F

This ——— published before.

They ——— a party tonight.

How many of you ——— here before?

Nearly everyone ——— some problems.

I ——— a cold for over a week.

John ——— many problems this week.

They ——— trouble with their car.

Mr. Smith ——— asked to be the president.

She ——— nothing but trouble with it ever since she
bought it.

Rats ——— the plague to the country.	brought
Clouds ——— rain.	bring
She is ——— us some things from Japan.	bringing
She ——— several things with her.	took (brought)

9 C

Mr. Johnson wants to ——— all his children over to the show.	take
The students ——— their books here every day.	bring
He ——— many things with him when he came.	brought
Father ——— the baby from Mother.	took
Will you ——— out two folders from that file cabinet and ——— them to me immediately?	take; bring
I ——— some food out of the freezer for our dinner.	took
She should ——— the pills before going to bed.	take
——— the cake out of the oven before 3 o'clock.	Take
My faithful dog usually ——— me the newspaper.	brings
Should I ——— this ladder to him?	take
The carpenter forgot to ——— his tools when he came to work yesterday morning so I ——— his car and ——— them to him.	bring; took; brought
He always ——— his things with him when he goes.	takes

9 D

The children ——— all their toys to me every day.	bring
Will you ——— the garbage can out to the front, please?	take

She ——— perfect attendance in that class.

He should ——— there yesterday.

13 D

He ——— very temperamental.

They ——— a special party for her.

He ——— there frequently during the past few weeks.

He ——— a lot of money during his lifetime.

I'm sure you ——— here before.

As long as I can remember, there ——— no one here by
that name.

They ——— that car for a long time.

China ——— several severe earthquakes.

I ——— trouble with my car.

My brother ——— several opportunities to visit Samoa.

Finally, the work ——— completed.

I ——— here for over two years.

They ——— in Italy and France.

It seems like they ——— trouble all their lives.

John and Mary ——— writing to each other for a long time.

13 E

It seems like we ——— here for years.

He ——— many trials in his life.

Who is going to ——— those packages here to the office?	bring
Will you ——— out the two folders from that file cabinet?	take
Will you ——— him to me as soon as he gets here?	bring
The policeman ——— the burglar in to be questioned after he caught him.	brought (took)
I ——— some food out of the freezer last night.	took
She always ——— her pills before going to bed.	takes
March always ——— spring rains.	brings
Mother asked me to ——— this ladder out to him.	take
She ——— the exam and failed it, so she'll ——— another one in a month.	took; take
I wasn't sure how long we'd be, so I ——— my lunch.	brought (took)
My grandmother always ——— presents with her wherever she goes and we are always excited about what she ——— us.	takes; brings

9 E

Be sure to ——— a camera with you.	take (bring)
Everyone always ——— his lunch to work.	brings (takes)
It may ——— a long time to finish this project.	take
We were invited to ——— guests.	bring
It ——— a long time to finish.	took
I'm not going to ——— a camera this time as I ——— one on our last trip and didn't use it.	bring (take); took
Spring showers usually ——— many flowers.	bring
He always ——— too much time to work and has no time to play.	takes
Although it ——— much time and effort to do it correctly, it will ——— you the satisfaction of a job well done.	takes; bring

It ——— a long time since it has rained here.

He ——— four cars in the past two years.

We ——— some good times and some bad ones during the past year.

They ———n't ——— any rain there for the past three months.

They ——— trouble before they came here and ——— a lot of trouble since they arrived.

Many of the students ——— this class before.

She ——— a good time now.

Some of the students ——— here for over two years.

One of them ——— here since 1971.

13 C

It ——— raining for several days now.

Why ———n't they ——— notified?

One of the boys ——— a party tonight.

We ———n't ——— any rain for a month.

The dean ——— several of the students meet with him this afternoon.

She ——— as good as she knows how to be.

We could ——— there by now if we had hurried.

——— he ——— the car fixed yet?

The car ——— fixed now.

He ——— three accidents this year.

We ——— a party tonight and want you to come.

One of the students ———n't ——— here for several days.

I'm afraid someone ——— hurt.

——— a warm coat as it might be cold there.   Take

How many of you ——— your lunch with you today?   brought

He ——— the exam last week, but I have to ——— it tomorrow.   took; take

9 F

Why don't you ——— your things and leave?   take

He ——— his friend over to meet us.   brought

She didn't ——— anything with her when she left.   take

——— me those books from the table over there.   Bring

He always ——— his lunch with him when he goes.   takes

Why didn't you ——— the baby over so I could watch him?   bring

If you ——— those things off the desk, ——— them over here   take; bring
to me.

He ——— in some fresh vegetables from the garden and   brought; took
——— the meat from the freezer.

Are we supposed to ——— our lunches when we go?   take

I have ——— all I can from my boss.   taken

She should have ——— her lunch with her.   brought (taken)

Are we supposed to ——— our lunches when we come?   bring

She always ——— some presents with her when she goes.   takes

13 A   *be* and *have* in combinations
                      as verbs and auxiliaries—
                      has had, has been, had been,
                      is having, are having, am having,
                      was having, were having, had had

They ——— a fight every night.

We ——— another get-together next week.

Why ———n't he ——— the car fixed?

I think she ——— enough time to finish the test.

She ——— guests for dinner tonight.

They ———n't ——— many opportunities before.

They ——— a Christmas party.

I ———n't ——— enough to do.

We ——— always ——— a car.

She ———n't ——— that very long.

She ——— a good time when we saw her last.

John ——— an accident.

He said he ———n't ——— enough notice.

They ——— a test in English today.

Mary ——— never ——— time to do it.

13 B

We ——— there several times already.

She ——— some trouble with her work in the lab.

They ——— friends in for dinner tonight.

He ——— good for over a month now; we haven't had any
trouble with him at all.

10 A   get, make, do

He barely manages to ——— by in his work.	get
He doesn't ——— any more than he has to.	do
That ——— me sick.	makes
She ——— most of her own clothes last year.	made
He's trying to ——— out of ——— the assignments.	get; doing
What do you expect to ——— from this class?	get
He wants to ——— some money this year.	make
He ——— a lot of friends on his trip.	made
What do you expect to ——— in this class?	do (make)
He wants to ——— ahead.	get
Where can I ——— my paycheck?	get
He ——— very well in his work.	does
How much money ——— he ———?	does; make

10 B

He always ——— his own breakfast.	makes (gets)
Why does he ——— that all the time?	do
Sometimes he ——— mad at everybody.	gets
It's too far for you to walk; let me ——— it for you.	get (do)
He always ——— a big fuss about things.	makes
He's afraid he'll ——— fired if he goes.	get
That ——— three days in a row that he's been late.	makes

You ——— due here an hour ago.

Where ——— the children gone and where will they ———
this evening?

He ——— coming tomorrow and will ——— here for six
weeks if we ——— a place for him.

You should ——— come to see me immediately.

There ——— been no one here by that name for the past
two years.

I ——— sure you're right.

12 F

She ——— it now, but John will ——— it tomorrow.

Check these figures and ——— them recorded immediately.

One of them ——— a cold and the other ——— out of town.

Come quickly as John ——— had a bad accident.

He is ——— very temperamental.

Although half of the apple is bad the other half could ———
eaten.

It can't ——— that late! It seems like we've only ——— here
for a short time.

John said he ——— bringing his friends over as they are ———
an impromptu party.

Where ——— all the time gone?

I can ——— ready in a minute as I only ——— to comb my
hair.

He said that he was ——— a new secretary.	getting
What has he ——— now?	done (got) (made)
He never ——— any excuses.	makes
He's always ——— into trouble.	getting
What does he think he's ———?	doing
How much is he ——— each week?	getting (making)
We have ——— several shipments lately.	gotten (got) (made)
He ——— a good salary.	gets

10 C

I ——— tired early, so I quit.	got
What ——— the wheels go around?	makes
She has ——— a lot of money.	made
He ——— a big raise.	got
Where did you ——— that?	get
The early bird ——— the worm.	gets
That should ——— it for now.	do
He is ——— his best, but he isn't ——— anywhere.	doing; getting
Why don't you ——— some good help?	get
She always ——— her own bread.	makes
He has ——— into trouble before.	gotten
They haven't ——— anything illegal yet.	done
She has always ——— her own bread.	made
The neighbors ——— a big fuss about it.	made

89

12 D

You should ——— known better than that.

They ——— there before I ———.

How many accidents ——— occurred on this corner?

Most of the children ——— hungry and tired.

He hasn't ——— an accident yet.

Why ——— he done that so often?

He should ——— ashamed of himself.

I think they ——— carried this too far.

Mary ——— late this morning.

The candidates ——— all confident they would win.

John is ——— a great time swimming.

He has ——— a lot of problems with his family.

He told me he ———n't been there in years.

Why haven't you ——— coming to class?

12 E

It can't ——— that bad.

What ——— he done this time?

The class ——— always prepared last year.

He should have ——— here an hour ago.

I think he'll ——— here any minute.

Mary just phoned and said John ——— had an accident.

257

10 D

We must ——— our work done right away.	get
He has ——— all he can at present.	done
He ——— his work well.	did (does)
What time ——— he usually ——— his work done?	does; get
He said he would ——— his work before he left.	do
He always ——— his work finished on time.	gets
They have ——— many mistakes in the past.	made
He always ——— his work on time.	does
I wish he would ——— up his mind about what he will ———.	make; do
She always ——— good grades.	gets (makes)
When does she ——— her homework?	do
She ——— herself some new clothes last week.	made
She was ——— her homework when I called.	doing

10 E

Somehow or other she seems to ——— by.	get
Singing seems to ——— the day go faster.	make
Where did you ——— that tool?	get
He always ——— a good job and ——— good money.	does; makes
He tried to ——— out of ——— the assignment.	get; doing
He ——— lots of friends while he was there.	made
He is ——— a good job, as he is trying to ——— ahead.	doing; get

He ——— several of them and there are others who ———
some too.

He ——— to be there on time every day.

They ——— gone before we got there.

It ——— a good thing I went to see him.

How many of you have ——— here before?

You can ——— it if you wish.

He doesn't ——— much money to spend.

Please bring some with you if you ——— any left.

Nearly everyone ——— had some problems in his life.

12 C

He ——— tried hard to learn English, and ——— still trying
hard to learn it.

——— you been here before?

Where ——— all the children gone?

One of the children ——— in the house.

Both of the girls ——— there yesterday.

Where ——— all the children?

At present, everyone ——— well except Mary; she ———
a cold.

I ———n't had a cold for years.

He has ——— many trials in his life.

Most of the boys ——— cheerfully done their work.

They are ——— trouble with their car.

He has ——— asked to be president.

They never ——— any trouble while they were there.

She always ——— excuses because she ——— so poorly.   makes; does

That ——— the third time he's ——— that.   makes; done

He is always ——— into trouble.   getting

10 F

He's always ——— things hard for us.   making

Why don't you ——— the tickets?   get

She ——— too many excuses.   makes

He's always ——— things the hard way.   doing

He ——— a lot of money, but it always seemed to ——— away from him.   made; get

What has he ——— that has ——— you so mad?   done; made

We ——— our best, but we ——— lots of mistakes.   did; made

He ——— into trouble when he ——— that before.   got; did

I ——— tired when I ——— all those things.   got; made

Why didn't you ——— here on time?   get

11 A   say, tell

He ——— he'd come tomorrow.   said

I haven't ——— him yet, but plan on it tomorrow.   told

What do you think he'll ——— when you ——— him?   say; tell

12 A

be and *have* as either verbs
or auxiliaries—*am, are, is, was,
were, be, been, being, has,
have, had*

He has ――― gone for a long time.

We ――― had a hard time getting our work done.

The meal ――― eaten quickly.

I ――― sure the president is right because he ――― authority.

We ――― to bring all our books to class every day.

We ――― always happy to see him when he comes.

There ――― a heavy rainstorm last week.

We asked about him, but they said he ――― left.

We ――― been unhappy with the results.

John hasn't ――― much time to prepare the report.

One of the boys ―――n't finished yet.

If anyone ――― a copy of the report I'd like to see it.

Most of the people ―― ― been here before.

There are several people present here who ――― at the
dedication last year.

12 B

We have ――― given many instructions.

This ――― been published before.

He can ――― good if he tries.

Please don't ――― so noisy.

They ――― coming to see us tonight.

He didn't ——— us his plans.   tell

She had already ——— me the news.   told

They didn't ——— anything about their plans.   say

John ——— he had been too busy to do it.   said

He ——— his wife that he would be late for dinner.   told

You really should ——— the truth about it.   tell

He ——— exactly what he thought about the project.   said

He ——— us that he didn't like the plan.   told

She is ——— all kinds of things about you.   saying

I ——— him it wasn't nice to ——— things like that.   told; say

11 B

She ——— us, and I'm sure she is going to ——— everyone.   told; tell

He didn't ——— why he was going.   say

She's been ——— a lot of things about you.   saying

He ——— he would ——— us before he ——— anyone else.   said; tell; told

She ——— her friend had ——— her about the announcement.   said; told

He ——— he had enjoyed his trip immensely.   said

He ——— he was ——— the truth.   said; telling

Mary ——— the children a story.   told

Most of his friends ——— him he is very handsome.   tell

I wouldn't ——— anything about it if I were you.   say

All of the girls ——— finished their work.

Why ———n't someone mended the fence?

They ——— a wonderful family.

One of the books ——— some pages missing.

One of you ——— to do the work.

11 G

She ——— always succeeded in everything.

He ——— always ——— a lot of money.

They ——— a lot of money left to them.

I ——— to go now.

They ——— three children before they left here.

He ——— ten dollars but he ——— spent it all.

He ——— worked here for the past two years.

Where ——— she been for the past hour?

What does that ——— to do with the subject?

It ——— taken us a long time to get here.

They have ——— some interesting experiences.

Why ——— she come?

We ——— three choices.

11 C

He ——— he hadn't done it, but she ——— everyone he had.	said; told
He didn't ——— why he had already ——— most of his friends.	say; told
She has been ——— that for years.	saying
He has ——— that story a dozen times.	told
She didn't ——— when she would be ready to ——— us her plans.	say; tell
Mary ——— me she wouldn't do it again.	told
Why didn't she ——— that before?	say
You really should have ——— them the truth.	told
He didn't ——— when he would be going.	say
I wonder why they didn't ——— anything about it to me?	say
I ——— exactly what I meant.	said
I didn't think she would ——— on me.	tell

11 D

Mr. Jones ——— that he thought his wife had ——— me about it.	said; told
Yesterday they ——— the children the truth.	told
He was so astonished he couldn't ——— anything.	say
She ——— that she had ——— you everything.	said; told
She is ——— everybody that you ——— that.	telling; said
I'm going to walk right up and ——— what I think.	say
She hasn't ——— she would go, but she hasn't ——— she wouldn't either.	said; said

We ——— many strange experiences on our trip.

He hasn't ——— many opportunities to speak English in the past.

We ——— several choices at this time.

He ——— his writings published.

What ——— you done with the tickets?

The work ——— never been completed.

They ——— been here for a long time.

He ——— a great interest in the program.

I ——— several copies so you may have one.

She ——— great talent.

11 F

He has ——— many interesting experiences in his life.

She ——— gone there several times.

He ———n't been here since yesterday.

We ——— finished long before the time was up.

He asked me if I ——— any money.

Why ——— you come to see me?

It ———n't rained here for a long time.

We ——— had lots of trouble.

I ——— an opportunity to go to school next year.

One of the boys ——— a cold and can't come.

He ――― that, didn't he?	said
Don't ――― anything about what he just ――― you.	say; told
She ――― that he always does that.	says

11 E

He ――― that the children had asked him to ――― them a story.	said; tell
I didn't think she ――― the word correctly, so I looked it up.	said
She ――― me not to ――― anyone else, and I ――― I wouldn't.	told; tell; said
I wish they'd ――― something about it.	say (said)
I don't think he'll ever ――― that story again.	tell
He ――― me his secret, but I can't ――― anything else.	told; say
Why doesn't she ――― something in English?	say
He ――― something, but I'm sure he didn't ――― the truth.	said; tell
He hasn't ――― anything about that for years.	said
Everyone is ――― something different about it.	saying

11 F

I didn't ――― him that she had already ――― me the news.	tell; told
He didn't ――― when he expected to go to California.	say
She just ――― that so people will listen to her.	says
He ――― that story to anyone who will listen; I think he's ――― it a dozen times.	tells; told
He didn't ――― us what he was going to ――― at the meeting.	tell; say

11 D

How many times ——— he told you about it?

He ——— done that several times.

She ——— her turn last week.

He has ——— several chances.

How many times ——— you told her about it?

They might ——— been there before.

Mary ——— broken her watch before she left.

He couldn't ——— done it.

How many times ——— you been there?

He ——— studied English before he came here.

We have ——— several chances to go.

Who ——— the time?

Who could ——— done that?

John ——— to go now.

He has done more than he should ——— done.

11 E

What ——— you done with my book?

He ——— finished his work before he came.

I ——— to finish my work before I can go.

She ——— a new dress for the party tonight.

What ——— he done with my book?

I'm not sure that I ——— you what he ———.   told; said

He couldn't have ——— them anything about it.   told

He ——— he thought that was the way it happened.   said

People are ——— they think you know something about it.   saying

He has ——— that before, and I've ——— him so.   said; told

12 A   want, need

She ——— her job here and doesn't ——— to leave it.   needs; want

He ——— to buy a new car although he doesn't need one.   wants

Does she ——— to be a teacher?   want

Students ——— to register before school starts.   need

If you ——— to see him you'll ——— to make an appointment.   want; need

If everyone comes you'll ——— more chairs.   need

How many textbooks will we ——— for that course?   need

Bring a coat if you think you'll ——— one.   need

Everyone ——— to go when they heard about it.   wanted

Bring only what you ——— as there is very little room.   need

What do I ——— to make a cake?   need

Bring it if you ——— to, but I don't think you'll ——— it.   want; need

Some of them are ——— trouble with it.

Have you ——— any trouble with it?

Why don't you ——— someone fix it who knows how?

They ——— had that car for a long time.

He ——— a good job last year.

Why doesn't he ——— someone fix it who knows how?

Mary has ——— several chances to go to Japan.

He's ——— a hard time learning English.

11 C

Mary never ——— time to do it.

If I ——— more time I'd do it myself.

He often ——— friends in for dinner.

They usually ——— a wonderful time.

He is ——— a lot of trouble.

Where ——— all the time gone?

I ——— seen that man before.

He ———n't seen her for a long time.

Where ——— all the people gone?

I ——— always had to hurry to get there on time.

She could ——— gone if she ——— wanted to.

Are they ——— friends in tonight?

They ——— a good time at the party.

Everyone ——— some problems.

12 B

We ——— chicken for dinner tomorrow.	want
You ——— a haircut.	need
The dean said he ——— to see you.	wanted
This lawn ——— mowing.	needs
He ——— to go to the dentist as he has a toothache.	needs
She ——— us to write an essay for homework.	wants
He ——— help! He's drowning.	needs
He ——— a hamburger for lunch.	wants
When she grows up, she ——— to be just like her mother.	wants
We ——— to store food and water in case of an emergency.	need
What do I ——— to do to help you?	need
His mother ——— her son to get a college education.	wants
This house ——— to be painted.	needs
The teacher ——— all the students to be present at the lecture.	wants (wanted)
He ——— to marry someone like his mother.	wants

12 C

What do I ——— to do to help you?	need
What do you ——— to eat tonight?	want
What will I ——— for the trip?	need
What do you ——— to do with your life?	want
Invite anyone you ——— to the party.	want

11 A

review of *have—*
have, has had

He ———n't had a chance to do much about it.

One of the girls ——— finished the test already.

——— anyone seen my paper? I ——— it a short while ago.

Where ——— everyone gone?

There ———n't been anyone around for a long time.

One of the boys is ——— a party tonight.

Which of you ——— the assignment for tonight?

I ——— had many different thoughts about the matter.

Mr. Jones could ——— gone to Suva.

We ———n't been anywhere for a long time.

He must ——— seen it somewhere.

If he ———n't seen it who ———?

They were ——— some trouble with their car, so I helped them.

11 B

One of the students ——— two copies of the assignments so he gave me one.

He could ——— finished if he ——— tried.

I'm ——— trouble with my boat motor.

She has ——— nothing but trouble with it ever since she bought it.

He is ——— his tooth pulled this afternoon.

One of them ——— a cold.

The student ——— to take eighteen hours although he only ——— to take twelve.	wants; needs
Parents usually ——— the best for their children.	want
He is overweight because he eats what he ——— instead of what he ———.	wants; needs
Students ——— a library clearance before they receive their grades.	need
He ——— to take his vacation in July.	wants
Bring everything you'll ——— because you won't be able to buy anything there.	need
What do you ——— for Christmas?	want
He needs help but doesn't ——— to ask for it.	want

12 D

If you ——— the job you'll ——— to impress the manager.	want; need
When do you ——— me to come?	want
He said he would call if he ——— anything.	needs (wants)
She makes enough money to buy everything she ———, but not everything she often ———.	needs; wants
The boys are trapped on the ledge and ——— help to get down.	need
Some day I ——— to travel and see the world, and I ——— to do it before I'm too old to enjoy it.	want; want
To make a good salad one ——— fresh produce.	needs
You will ——— to look after your sister while I'm gone.	need
If he could have everything he ———, he thinks he would be happy.	wants

He can't have ――― that many failures.

You really should ――― your teeth fixed.

He may ――― some trouble with the immigration office
as he has ――― some in the past.

Why hasn't anyone ――― this fixed?

John might ――― it if Mary doesn't.

They were ――― a hard time when I left.

He might be ――― a party tonight.

The library might ――― the books you want.

10 F

We really haven't ――― a lot of fun here.

I heard that Mary is ――― a party tonight.

She's ――― a cold for a week.

I've ――― that coat for a long time and wish I could ―――
a new one.

All the students are ――― trouble with that problem.

Bring it over if you're ――― trouble so I can ――― a look
at it.

John may ――― trouble starting the car as I have often
――― problems starting it.

His parents are ――― trouble again.

They have never ――― any trouble with it before.

He should ――― my book as I loaned it to him last week.

She has ――― a lot of colds this year.

They're ――― several students come over tonight.